OUR FAMILY TREE & ALBUM

Memory Press

Published by Memory Press
P.O. Box 327
Poole
Dorset BH15 2RG

© The Five Mile Press Pty. Ltd. 1987

UK Edition Reprinted 1991

Printed in Singapore by Kyodo Printing Co. Ltd.

ISBN 0 86788 221 2

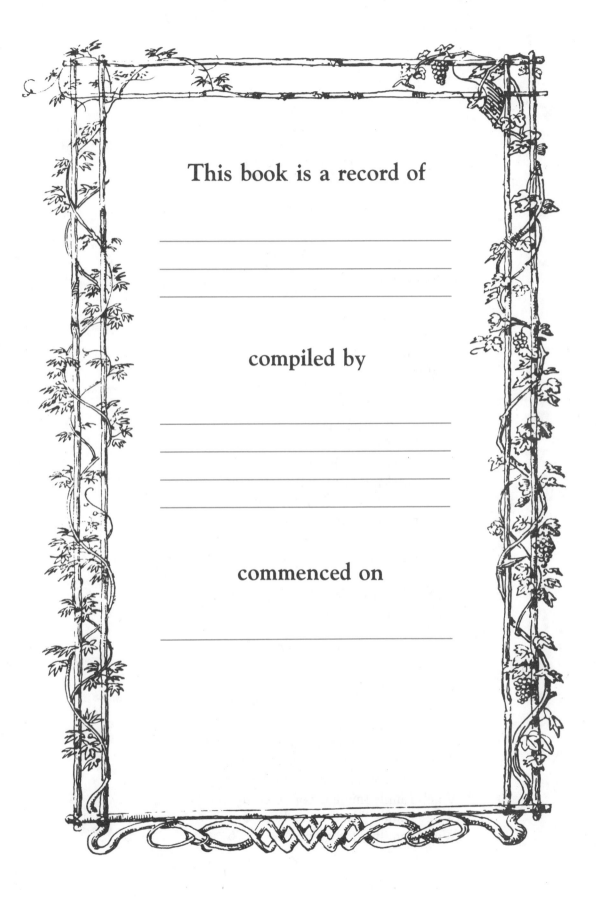

This book is a record of

_____

_____

_____

compiled by

_____

_____

_____

_____

commenced on

_____

Contents

Introduction   8

Husband's Genealogy   12
Wife's Genealogy   13
Our Children   14
Our Grandchildren   16
Our Family Tree   18

Husband's Family Tree   22
Husband's Family   26
Husband's Father's Family   28
Husband's Mother's Family   30
Husband's Paternal Grandparents   32
Husband's Maternal Grandparents   36
Husband's Paternal Great-Grandparents   40
Husband's Maternal Great-Grandparents   42
Husband's Family Immigration Record   44
Husband's Family War Service Record   46
Husband's Family Photographs   48

Wife's Family Tree   50
Wife's Family   54
Wife's Father's Family   56
Wife's Mother's Family   58
Wife's Paternal Grandparents   60
Wife's Maternal Grandparents   64
Wife's Paternal Great-Grandparents   68
Wife's Maternal Great-Grandparents   70
Wife's Family Immigration Record   72
Wife's Family War Service Record   74
Wife's Family Photographs   76

Weddings   78
Wedding Photographs   82
Religious Ceremonies   84
Where We Worship   85
Lest We Forget   86
Our Family Homes   90
Homes of our ancestors   92
Schools Attended   94
Membership of Clubs and Organizations   98
Employment Profiles   100
Family Business Enterprises   102
Family Sporting Activities   104
Special Friends   106
Family Pets   108
Family Vehicles   110
Family Holidays   112
Heirlooms and Family Collections   114
Special Family Occasions   118
Family Traditions   122
Storytellers   124

Introduction

Has your family ever kept a central record of facts and photographs, or do you have to keep asking who your ancestors were and where they come from? Is there a photograph of your great grandparents? Did your father or grandfather do National Service, or fight in the War? Keeping an official record can not only be fun, it can be doing the rest of the family a real service.

Checking your family tree back two or three generations can be even more fun. Perhaps one of your ancestors was deported to Australia for some trivial offence, and never returned? Perhaps you have Royal blood in the family? It is said that if anyone digs deep enough into their genealogy, they always find a murderer!

In completing the details outlined in the following pages individuals will face varying degrees of difficulty; some will have very little trouble going back several generations, while others will draw a blank after perhaps only one generation. To find the answers the most obvious line of approach is to work from the known to the unknown, in a step by step progression.

As the tables suggest, begin with your immediate family. Complete as many of the details as possible yourself and then seek further answers from the other members of your family. Simply by chatting among family members, both general and specific information will be forthcoming. After the personal contact, the next step is to seek out family Bibles, albums, diaries and letters.

Now turn to information from public records; birth, marriage and death certificates, wills, land deeds, parish registers and inscriptions on the headstones of graves. In all requests for information, include as many known facts as possible, however trivial they may seem, and remember that over successive generations many names have altered: foreign names may have been anglicised and in other instances names have been misspelt in Parish registers.

The Parish records are the first place to start checking, if you know the Parish in which your parents were married, or born. An additional source of local information is the archive or reference department of the local library or newspaper. For national births, deaths and marriage records in England and Wales, remember that the location in London is no longer Somerset House, but St Katherine's House, on Queensway, W2. Elsewhere, you can discover the address of your Public Records Office from the 'phone book.

Don't stop in your home country! If your ancestors arrived from another European country, or from the Commonwealth, try and determine the approximate year of arrival, and confirm it against the shipping records. These provide details of the port of embarkation and can be the stepping stone to overseas research. Similarly, if any branch of the family has emigrated, shipping records are a good place to start checking.

This stage can become expensive if you elect to carry out the research personally or pay a professional researcher. However, many gaps can be filled by corresponding with the various public offices and other authorities. Again, supply as many known details as possible and include any necessary payments, particularly return postage, and don't be impatient; it takes time.

Further guidance in seeking out answers can be obtained from genealogical and historical societies. Who knows — once you have filled all the gaps you may well proceed to write your family history.
Good luck!

Possible contacts:

The Society of Genealogists,
14 Charterhouse Buildings,
London EC1M 7BA

The Heraldry Society,
44-45 Museum Street,
London WC1

Heraldry Today,
10 Beauchamp Place,
London SW3

The Genealogy Bookshop,
3 Nassau Street,
Dublin 2,
Ireland

British Association for Local History,
The Mill Managers House,
Cromford Mill,
Cromford,
Matlock,
Derbyshire DE4 3RQ

PLACE
PHOTOGRAPH
HERE

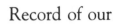

Record of our

Certificate of Marriage

Married by

_____

NAME OF MINISTER   PRIEST   MARRIAGE CELEBRANT

at

_____

on

_____

between

_____

BRIDEGROOM

and

_____

BRIDE

in the presence of

_____

WITNESS   WITNESS

PLACE
PHOTOGRAPH
HERE

Husband's Genealogy

FULL NAME

DATE OF BIRTH

PLACE OF BIRTH

FATHER'S FULL NAME

MOTHER'S FULL NAME

BROTHERS

SISTERS

PLACE
PHOTOGRAPH
HERE

Wife's Genealogy

FULL NAME

DATE OF BIRTH

PLACE OF BIRTH

FATHER'S FULL NAME

MOTHER'S FULL NAME

BROTHERS

SISTERS

Our Children

FULL NAME

TIME AND DATE OF BIRTH

PLACE OF BIRTH

_____

_____

_____

_____

_____

_____

_____

_____

_____

SPECIAL COMMENTS

_____

PLACE
PHOTOGRAPH
HERE

PLACE
PHOTOGRAPH
HERE

PLACE
PHOTOGRAPH
HERE

BABY PHOTOGRAPHS

Our Grandchildren

NAME	PARENTS	DATE OF BIRTH	PLACE OF BIRTH

_____
_____
_____
_____
_____
_____
_____
_____
_____
_____
_____
_____
_____

NAME	PARENTS	DATE OF BIRTH	PLACE OF BIRTH

HUSBAND'S FULL NAME

WIFE'S FULL NAME

DATE OF MARRIAGE

PLACE OF MARRIAGE

CHILDREN

Our
Family Tree

HUSBAND'S PATERNAL GRANDFATHER'S FULL NAME

HUSBAND'S PATERNAL GRANDMOTHER'S FULL NAME

DATE OF MARRIAGE

PLACE OF MARRIAGE

CHILDREN

HUSBAND'S FATHER'S FULL NAME

HUSBAND'S MOTHER'S FULL NAME

DATE OF MARRIAGE

PLACE OF MARRIAGE

CHILDREN

HUSBAND'S MATERNAL GRANDFATHER'S FULL NAME

HUSBAND'S MATERNAL GRANDMOTHER'S FULL NAME

DATE OF MARRIAGE

PLACE OF MARRIAGE

CHILDREN

WIFE'S PATERNAL GRANDFATHER'S FULL NAME

WIFE'S PATERNAL GRANDMOTHER'S FULL NAME

DATE OF MARRIAGE

PLACE OF MARRIAGE

CHILDREN

WIFE'S FATHER'S FULL NAME

WIFE'S MOTHER'S FULL NAME

DATE OF MARRIAGE

PLACE OF MARRIAGE

CHILDREN

WIFE'S MATERNAL GRANDFATHER'S FULL NAME

WIFE'S MATERNAL GRANDMOTHER'S FULL NAME

DATE OF MARRIAGE

PLACE OF MARRIAGE

CHILDREN

HUSBAND'S GREAT-GRANDFATHER'S FULL NAME

HUSBAND'S GREAT-GRANDMOTHER'S FULL NAME

HUSBAND'S GREAT-GRANDFATHER'S FULL NAME

HUSBAND'S GREAT-GRANDMOTHER'S FULL NAME

HUSBAND'S GREAT-GRANDFATHER'S FULL NAME

HUSBAND'S GREAT-GRANDMOTHER'S FULL NAME

HUSBAND'S GREAT-GRANDFATHER'S FULL NAME

HUSBAND'S GREAT-GRANDMOTHER'S FULL NAME

HUSBAND'S GREAT, GREAT-GRANDFATHER'S FULL NAME

HUSBAND'S GREAT, GREAT-GRANDMOTHER'S FULL NAME

HUSBAND'S GREAT, GREAT-GRANDFATHER'S FULL NAME

HUSBAND'S GREAT, GREAT-GRANDMOTHER'S FULL NAME

HUSBAND'S GREAT, GREAT-GRANDFATHER'S FULL NAME

HUSBAND'S GREAT, GREAT-GRANDMOTHER'S FULL NAME

HUSBAND'S GREAT, GREAT-GRANDFATHER'S FULL NAME

HUSBAND'S GREAT, GREAT-GRANDMOTHER'S FULL NAME

HUSBAND'S GREAT, GREAT-GRANDFATHER'S FULL NAME

HUSBAND'S GREAT, GREAT-GRANDMOTHER'S FULL NAME

HUSBAND'S GREAT, GREAT-GRANDFATHER'S FULL NAME

HUSBAND'S GREAT, GREAT-GRANDMOTHER'S FULL NAME

HUSBAND'S GREAT, GREAT-GRANDFATHER'S FULL NAME

HUSBAND'S GREAT, GREAT-GRANDMOTHER'S FULL NAME

HUSBAND'S GREAT, GREAT-GRANDFATHER'S FULL NAME

HUSBAND'S GREAT, GREAT-GRANDMOTHER'S FULL NAME

WIFE'S GREAT-GRANDFATHER'S FULL NAME

WIFE'S GREAT-GRANDMOTHER'S FULL NAME

WIFE'S GREAT-GRANDFATHER'S FULL NAME

WIFE'S GREAT-GRANDMOTHER'S FULL NAME

WIFE'S GREAT-GRANDFATHER'S FULL NAME

WIFE'S GREAT-GRANDMOTHER'S FULL NAME

WIFE'S GREAT-GRANDFATHER'S FULL NAME

WIFE'S GREAT-GRANDMOTHER'S FULL NAME

WIFE'S GREAT, GREAT-GRANDFATHER'S FULL NAME

WIFE'S GREAT, GREAT-GRANDMOTHER'S FULL NAME

WIFE'S GREAT, GREAT-GRANDFATHER'S FULL NAME

WIFE'S GREAT, GREAT-GRANDMOTHER'S FULL NAME

WIFE'S GREAT, GREAT-GRANDFATHER'S FULL NAME

WIFE'S GREAT, GREAT-GRANDMOTHER'S FULL NAME

WIFE'S GREAT, GREAT-GRANDFATHER'S FULL NAME

WIFE'S GREAT, GREAT-GRANDMOTHER'S FULL NAME

WIFE'S GREAT, GREAT-GRANDFATHER'S FULL NAME

WIFE'S GREAT, GREAT-GRANDMOTHER'S FULL NAME

WIFE'S GREAT, GREAT–GRANDFATHER'S FULL NAME

WIFE'S GREAT, GREAT-GRANDMOTHER'S FULL NAME

WIFE'S GREAT, GREAT–GRANDFATHER'S FULL NAME

WIFE'S GREAT, GREAT–GRANDMOTHER'S FULL NAME

WIFE'S GREAT, GREAT–GRANDFATHER'S FULL NAME

WIFE'S GREAT, GREAT–GRANDMOTHER'S FULL NAME

MR & MRS _____
GREAT, GREAT, GREAT-GRANDPARENTS

SPECIAL COMMENTS

MR & MRS _____
GREAT, GREAT, GREAT-GRANDPARENTS

MR & MRS _____
GREAT, GREAT, GREAT-GRANDPARENTS

MR & MRS _____
GREAT, GREAT, GREAT-GRANDPARENTS

MR & MRS _____
GREAT, GREAT, GREAT-GRANDPARENTS

MR & MRS _____
GREAT, GREAT, GREAT-GRANDPARENTS

MR & MRS _____
GREAT, GREAT, GREAT-GRANDPARENTS

MR & MRS _____
GREAT, GREAT, GREAT-GRANDPARENTS

MR & MRS _____
GREAT, GREAT, GREAT-GRANDPARENTS

MR & MRS _____
GREAT, GREAT, GREAT-GRANDPARENTS

MR & MRS _____
GREAT, GREAT, GREAT-GRANDPARENTS

MR & MRS _____
GREAT, GREAT, GREAT-GRANDPARENTS

MR & MRS _____
GREAT, GREAT, GREAT-GRANDPARENTS

MR & MRS _____
GREAT, GREAT, GREAT-GRANDPARENTS

MR & MRS _____
GREAT, GREAT, GREAT-GRANDPARENTS

MR & MRS _____
GREAT, GREAT, GREAT-GRANDPARENTS

MR & MRS _____
GREAT, GREAT, GREAT-GRANDPARENTS

MR & MRS _____
GREAT, GREAT, GREAT-GRANDPARENTS

MR & MRS _____
GREAT, GREAT, GREAT-GRANDPARENTS

MR & MRS _____
GREAT, GREAT, GREAT-GRANDPARENTS

MR & MRS _____
GREAT, GREAT, GREAT-GRANDPARENTS

MR & MRS _____
GREAT, GREAT, GREAT-GRANDPARENTS

MR & MRS _____
GREAT, GREAT, GREAT-GRANDPARENTS

MR & MRS _____
GREAT, GREAT, GREAT-GRANDPARENTS

MR & MRS _____
GREAT, GREAT, GREAT-GRANDPARENTS

MR & MRS _____
GREAT, GREAT, GREAT-GRANDPARENTS

MR & MRS _____
GREAT, GREAT, GREAT-GRANDPARENTS

MR & MRS _____
GREAT, GREAT, GREAT-GRANDPARENTS

MR & MRS _____
GREAT, GREAT, GREAT-GRANDPARENTS

MR & MRS _____
GREAT, GREAT, GREAT-GRANDPARENTS

MR & MRS _____
GREAT, GREAT, GREAT-GRANDPARENTS

MR & MRS _____
GREAT, GREAT, GREAT-GRANDPARENTS

Husband's Family Tree

HUSBAND'S FULL NAME

DATE OF BIRTH

PLACE OF BIRTH

DATE OF MARRIAGE

PLACE OF MARRIAGE

OCCUPATION

SPECIAL INTERESTS

GRANDFATHER'S FULL NAME

DATE OF BIRTH

PLACE OF BIRTH

DATE OF MARRIAGE

PLACE OF MARRIAGE

OCCUPATION

SPECIAL INTERESTS

FATHER'S FULL NAME

DATE OF BIRTH

PLACE OF BIRTH

DATE OF MARRIAGE

PLACE OF MARRIAGE

OCCUPATION

SPECIAL INTERESTS

GRANDMOTHER'S FULL NAME

DATE OF BIRTH

PLACE OF BIRTH

DATE OF MARRIAGE

PLACE OF MARRIAGE

OCCUPATION

SPECIAL INTERESTS

GRANDFATHER'S FULL NAME

DATE OF BIRTH

PLACE OF BIRTH

DATE OF MARRIAGE

PLACE OF MARRIAGE

OCCUPATION

SPECIAL INTERESTS

MOTHER'S FULL NAME

DATE OF BIRTH

PLACE OF BIRTH

DATE OF MARRIAGE

PLACE OF MARRIAGE

OCCUPATION

SPECIAL INTERESTS

GRANDMOTHER'S FULL NAME

DATE OF BIRTH

PLACE OF BIRTH

DATE OF MARRIAGE

PLACE OF MARRIAGE

OCCUPATION

SPECIAL INTERESTS

GREAT-GRANDFATHER'S FULL NAME
_____

DATE OF BIRTH   PLACE OF BIRTH
_____
                    OCCUPATION

GREAT-GRANDMOTHER'S FULL NAME
_____

DATE OF BIRTH   PLACE OF BIRTH
_____
                    SPECIAL INTERESTS

GREAT-GRANDFATHER'S FULL NAME
_____

DATE OF BIRTH   PLACE OF BIRTH
_____
                    OCCUPATION

GREAT-GRANDMOTHER'S FULL NAME
_____

DATE OF BIRTH   PLACE OF BIRTH
_____
                    SPECIAL INTERESTS

GREAT-GRANDFATHER'S FULL NAME
_____

DATE OF BIRTH   PLACE OF BIRTH
_____
                    OCCUPATION

GREAT-GRANDMOTHER'S FULL NAME
_____

DATE OF BIRTH   PLACE OF BIRTH
_____
                    SPECIAL INTERESTS

GREAT-GRANDFATHER'S FULL NAME
_____

DATE OF BIRTH   PLACE OF BIRTH
_____
                    OCCUPATION

GREAT-GRANDMOTHER'S FULL NAME
_____

DATE OF BIRTH   PLACE OF BIRTH
_____
                    SPECIAL INTERESTS

GREAT, GREAT-GRANDFATHER'S FULL NAME
_____

GREAT, GREAT-GRANDMOTHER'S FULL NAME
_____

GREAT, GREAT-GRANDFATHER'S FULL NAME
_____

GREAT, GREAT-GRANDMOTHER'S FULL NAME
_____

GREAT, GREAT-GRANDFATHER'S FULL NAME
_____

GREAT, GREAT-GRANDMOTHER'S FULL NAME
_____

GREAT, GREAT-GRANDFATHER'S FULL NAME
_____

GREAT, GREAT-GRANDMOTHER'S FULL NAME
_____

GREAT, GREAT-GRANDFATHER'S FULL NAME
_____

GREAT, GREAT-GRANDMOTHER'S FULL NAME
_____

GREAT, GREAT-GRANDFATHER'S FULL NAME
_____

GREAT, GREAT-GRANDMOTHER'S FULL NAME
_____

GREAT, GREAT-GRANDFATHER'S FULL NAME
_____

GREAT, GREAT-GRANDMOTHER'S FULL NAME
_____

GREAT, GREAT-GRANDFATHER'S FULL NAME
_____

GREAT, GREAT-GRANDMOTHER'S FULL NAME
_____

GREAT, GREAT, GREAT-GRANDPARENTS   MR & MRS   NEE _____

GREAT, GREAT, GREAT-GRANDPARENTS   MR & MRS   NEE _____

GREAT, GREAT, GREAT-GRANDPARENTS   MR & MRS   NEE _____

GREAT, GREAT, GREAT-GRANDPARENTS   MR & MRS   NEE _____

GREAT, GREAT, GREAT-GRANDPARENTS   MR & MRS   NEE _____

GREAT, GREAT, GREAT-GRANDPARENTS   MR & MRS   NEE _____

GREAT, GREAT, GREAT-GRANDPARENTS   MR & MRS   NEE _____

GREAT, GREAT, GREAT-GRANDPARENTS   MR & MRS   NEE _____

GREAT, GREAT, GREAT-GRANDPARENTS   MR & MRS   NEE _____

GREAT, GREAT, GREAT-GRANDPARENTS   MR & MRS   NEE _____

GREAT, GREAT, GREAT-GRANDPARENTS   MR & MRS   NEE _____

GREAT, GREAT, GREAT-GRANDPARENTS   MR & MRS   NEE _____

GREAT, GREAT, GREAT-GRANDPARENTS   MR & MRS   NEE _____

GREAT, GREAT, GREAT-GRANDPARENTS   MR & MRS   NEE _____

GREAT, GREAT, GREAT-GRANDPARENTS   MR & MRS   NEE _____

GREAT, GREAT, GREAT-GRANDPARENTS   MR & MRS   NEE _____

GREAT, GREAT, GREAT-GRANDPARENTS   MR & MRS   NEE _____

GREAT, GREAT, GREAT-GRANDPARENTS   MR & MRS   NEE _____

GREAT, GREAT, GREAT-GRANDPARENTS   MR & MRS   NEE _____

GREAT, GREAT, GREAT-GRANDPARENTS   MR & MRS   NEE _____

GREAT, GREAT, GREAT-GRANDPARENTS   MR & MRS   NEE _____

GREAT, GREAT, GREAT-GRANDPARENTS   MR & MRS   NEE _____

GREAT, GREAT, GREAT-GRANDPARENTS   MR & MRS   NEE _____

GREAT, GREAT, GREAT-GRANDPARENTS   MR & MRS   NEE _____

GREAT, GREAT, GREAT-GRANDPARENTS   MR & MRS   NEE _____

GREAT, GREAT, GREAT-GRANDPARENTS   MR & MRS   NEE _____

GREAT, GREAT, GREAT-GRANDPARENTS   MR & MRS   NEE _____

GREAT, GREAT, GREAT-GRANDPARENTS   MR & MRS   NEE _____

GREAT, GREAT, GREAT-GRANDPARENTS   MR & MRS   NEE _____

GREAT, GREAT, GREAT-GRANDPARENTS   MR & MRS   NEE _____

GREAT, GREAT, GREAT-GRANDPARENTS   MR & MRS   NEE _____

GREAT, GREAT, GREAT-GRANDPARENTS   MR & MRS   NEE _____

HUSBAND'S
PHOTOGRAPH

Husband's Family
HIS BROTHERS AND SISTERS, NIECES AND NEPHEWS

NAME	BORN	DIED	SPOUSE	CHILDREN

SPECIAL INTERESTS

_____
_____
_____
_____
_____
_____
_____
_____
_____
_____
_____
_____
_____
_____

NAME	BORN	DIED	SPOUSE	CHILDREN

PLACE
PHOTOGRAPH
HERE

PLACE
PHOTOGRAPH
HERE

PLACE
PHOTOGRAPH
HERE

Husband's Father's Family
HIS FATHER, HIS UNCLES AND AUNTS AND COUSINS

NAME	BORN	DIED	SPOUSE	CHILDREN

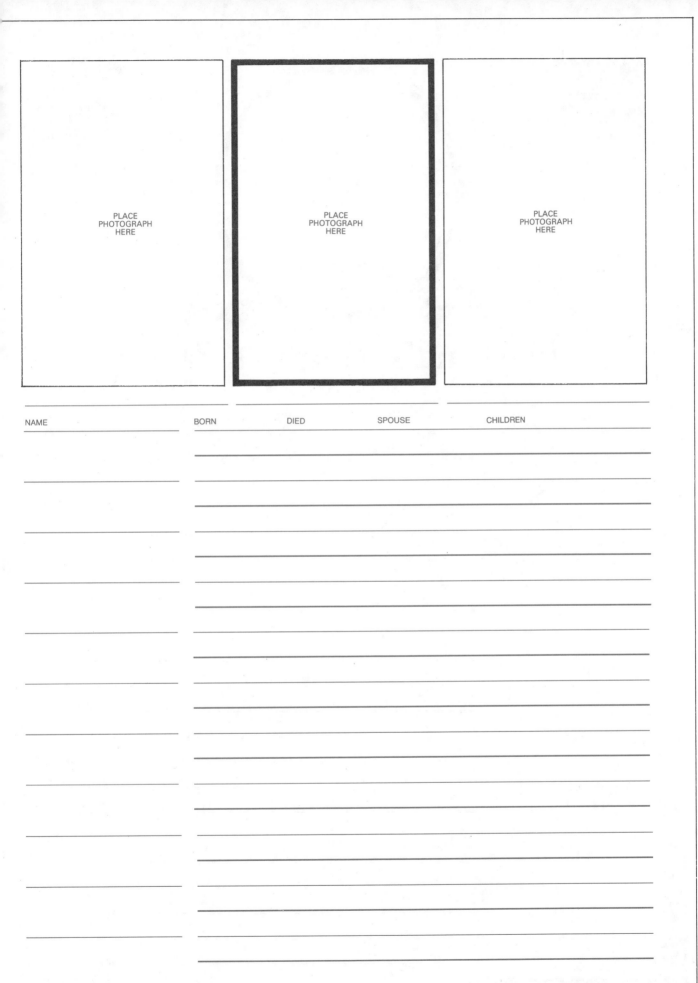

PLACE PHOTOGRAPH HERE

PLACE PHOTOGRAPH HERE

PLACE PHOTOGRAPH HERE

NAME   BORN   DIED   SPOUSE   CHILDREN

HUSBAND'S
MOTHER'S
PHOTOGRAPH

Husband's Mother's Family
HIS MOTHER, HIS UNCLES AND AUNTS AND COUSINS

NAME	BORN	DIED	SPOUSE	CHILDREN

NAME   BORN   DIED   SPOUSE   CHILDREN

PLACE
PHOTOGRAPH
HERE

PLACE
PHOTOGRAPH
HERE

PLACE
PHOTOGRAPH
HERE

SPECIAL COMMENTS

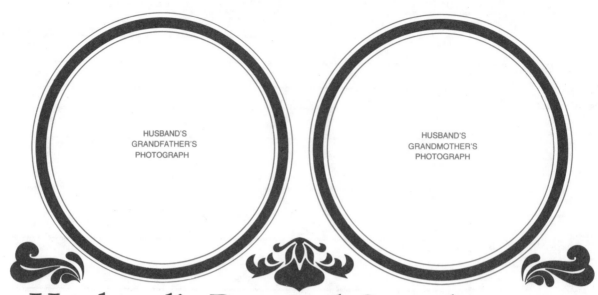

Husband's Paternal Grandparents

HUSBAND'S GRANDFATHER, HIS GREAT-AUNTS AND UNCLES AND THEIR CHILDREN

NAME	BORN	DIED	SPOUSE	CHILDREN

PLACE
PHOTOGRAPH
HERE

PLACE
PHOTOGRAPH
HERE

PLACE
PHOTOGRAPH
HERE

NAME   BORN   DIED   SPOUSE   CHILDREN

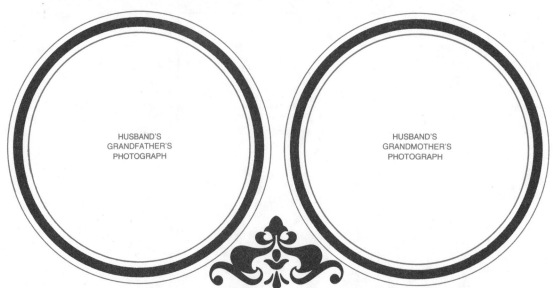

Husband's Paternal Grandparents
HUSBAND'S GRANDMOTHER, HIS GREAT-AUNTS AND UNCLES
AND THEIR CHILDREN

NAME	BORN	DIED	SPOUSE	CHILDREN

SPECIAL INTERESTS

_____
_____
_____
_____
_____
_____
_____
_____
_____
_____
_____
_____
_____
_____

NAME	BORN	DIED	SPOUSE	CHILDREN

PLACE
PHOTOGRAPH
HERE

PLACE
PHOTOGRAPH
HERE

PLACE
PHOTOGRAPH
HERE

Husband's Maternal Grandparents
HUSBAND'S GRANDFATHER, HIS GREAT-AUNTS AND UNCLES AND THEIR CHILDREN

NAME	BORN	DIED	SPOUSE	CHILDREN

SPECIAL COMMENTS

NAME   BORN   DIED   SPOUSE   CHILDREN

CHILDREN   CHILDREN

PLACE
PHOTOGRAPH
HERE

PLACE
PHOTOGRAPH
HERE

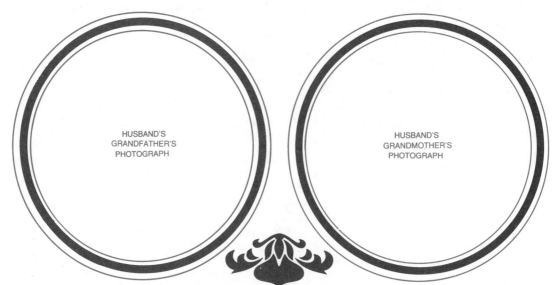

Husband's Maternal Grandparents
HUSBAND'S GRANDMOTHER, HIS GREAT-AUNTS AND UNCLES AND THEIR CHILDREN

NAME	BORN	DIED	SPOUSE	CHILDREN

NAME   BORN   DIED   SPOUSE   CHILDREN

PLACE
PHOTOGRAPH
HERE

PLACE
PHOTOGRAPH
HERE

PLACE
PHOTOGRAPH
HERE

Husband's Paternal Great~Grandparents

GREAT-GRANDFATHER

NAME	BORN	DIED	SPOUSE	CHILDREN

Husband's Paternal
Great~Grandparents

GREAT-GRANDMOTHER

NAME   BORN   DIED   SPOUSE   CHILDREN

INTERESTING DETAILS

Husband's Maternal Great~Grandparents

GREAT-GRANDFATHER

NAME	BORN	DIED	SPOUSE	CHILDREN

SPECIAL COMMENTS

Husband's Maternal Great~Grandparents

GREAT-GRANDMOTHER

NAME _____ BORN _____ DIED _____ SPOUSE _____ CHILDREN _____

SPECIAL COMMENTS

Husband's Family Immigration Record

From where did your descendants originally come? When?
How? Why? Where relevant include date of citizenship and as
much additional information as possible.

NAME	EMIGRATED FROM	TO	DATE	TRANSPORT

Add any information describing the migration of your family
within this country and so outline how your branch of the
family came to settle where it is today.

NAME	EMIGRATED FROM	TO	DATE	TRANSPORT

Husband's Family
War Service Record

NAME

RANK

WHERE SERVED

SPECIAL AWARDS

ADDITIONAL INFORMATION

NAME

RANK

WHERE SERVED

SPECIAL AWARDS

ADDITIONAL INFORMATION

NAME

RANK

WHERE SERVED

SPECIAL AWARDS

ADDITIONAL INFORMATION

NAME

RANK

WHERE SERVED

SPECIAL AWARDS

ADDITIONAL INFORMATION

NAME

RANK

WHERE SERVED

SPECIAL AWARDS

ADDITIONAL INFORMATION

NAME

RANK

WHERE SERVED

SPECIAL AWARDS

ADDITIONAL INFORMATION

NAME

RANK

WHERE SERVED

SPECIAL AWARDS

ADDITIONAL INFORMATION

NAME

RANK

WHERE SERVED

SPECIAL AWARDS

ADDITIONAL INFORMATION

Husband's Family
Photographs

NAME	DATE	INTERESTING DETAILS	PLACE

Wife's Family Tree

WIFE'S FULL NAME

DATE OF BIRTH

PLACE OF BIRTH

DATE OF MARRIAGE

PLACE OF MARRIAGE

OCCUPATION

SPECIAL INTERESTS

GRANDFATHER'S FULL NAME

DATE OF BIRTH

PLACE OF BIRTH

DATE OF MARRIAGE

PLACE OF MARRIAGE

OCCUPATION

SPECIAL INTERESTS

FATHER'S FULL NAME

DATE OF BIRTH

PLACE OF BIRTH

DATE OF MARRIAGE

PLACE OF MARRIAGE

OCCUPATION

SPECIAL INTERESTS

GRANDMOTHER'S FULL NAME

DATE OF BIRTH

PLACE OF BIRTH

DATE OF MARRIAGE

PLACE OF MARRIAGE

OCCUPATION

SPECIAL INTERESTS

GRANDFATHER'S FULL NAME

DATE OF BIRTH

PLACE OF BIRTH

DATE OF MARRIAGE

PLACE OF MARRIAGE

OCCUPATION

SPECIAL INTERESTS

MOTHER'S FULL NAME

DATE OF BIRTH

PLACE OF BIRTH

DATE OF MARRIAGE

PLACE OF MARRIAGE

OCCUPATION

SPECIAL INTERESTS

GRANDMOTHER'S FULL NAME

DATE OF BIRTH

PLACE OF BIRTH

DATE OF MARRIAGE

PLACE OF MARRIAGE

OCCUPATION

SPECIAL INTERESTS

GREAT-GRANDFATHER'S FULL NAME

DATE OF BIRTH   PLACE OF BIRTH

OCCUPATION

GREAT-GRANDMOTHER'S FULL NAME

DATE OF BIRTH   PLACE OF BIRTH

SPECIAL INTERESTS

GREAT-GRANDFATHER'S FULL NAME

DATE OF BIRTH   PLACE OF BIRTH

OCCUPATION

GREAT-GRANDMOTHER'S FULL NAME

DATE OF BIRTH   PLACE OF BIRTH

SPECIAL INTERESTS

GREAT-GRANDFATHER'S FULL NAME

DATE OF BIRTH   PLACE OF BIRTH

OCCUPATION

GREAT-GRANDMOTHER'S FULL NAME

DATE OF BIRTH   PLACE OF BIRTH

SPECIAL INTERESTS

GREAT-GRANDFATHER'S FULL NAME

DATE OF BIRTH   PLACE OF BIRTH

OCCUPATION

GREAT-GRANDMOTHER'S FULL NAME

DATE OF BIRTH   PLACE OF BIRTH

SPECIAL INTERESTS

GREAT, GREAT-GRANDFATHER'S FULL NAME

GREAT, GREAT-GRANDMOTHER'S FULL NAME

GREAT, GREAT-GRANDFATHER'S FULL NAME

GREAT, GREAT-GRANDMOTHER'S FULL NAME

GREAT, GREAT-GRANDFATHER'S FULL NAME

GREAT, GREAT-GRANDMOTHER'S FULL NAME

GREAT, GREAT-GRANDFATHER'S FULL NAME

GREAT, GREAT-GRANDMOTHER'S FULL NAME

GREAT, GREAT-GRANDFATHER'S FULL NAME

GREAT, GREAT-GRANDMOTHER'S FULL NAME

GREAT, GREAT-GRANDFATHER'S FULL NAME

GREAT, GREAT-GRANDMOTHER'S FULL NAME

GREAT, GREAT-GRANDFATHER'S FULL NAME

GREAT, GREAT-GRANDMOTHER'S FULL NAME

GREAT, GREAT-GRANDFATHER'S FULL NAME

GREAT, GREAT-GRANDMOTHER'S FULL NAME

GREAT, GREAT, GREAT-GRANDPARENTS	MR & MRS	NEE
GREAT, GREAT, GREAT-GRANDPARENTS	MR & MRS	NEE
GREAT, GREAT, GREAT-GRANDPARENTS	MR & MRS	NEE
GREAT, GREAT, GREAT-GRANDPARENTS	MR & MRS	NEE
GREAT, GREAT, GREAT-GRANDPARENTS	MR & MRS	NEE
GREAT, GREAT, GREAT-GRANDPARENTS	MR & MRS	NEE
GREAT, GREAT, GREAT-GRANDPARENTS	MR & MRS	NEE
GREAT, GREAT, GREAT-GRANDPARENTS	MR & MRS	NEE
GREAT, GREAT, GREAT-GRANDPARENTS	MR & MRS	NEE
GREAT, GREAT, GREAT-GRANDPARENTS	MR & MRS	NEE
GREAT, GREAT, GREAT-GRANDPARENTS	MR & MRS	NEE
GREAT, GREAT, GREAT-GRANDPARENTS	MR & MRS	NEE
GREAT, GREAT, GREAT-GRANDPARENTS	MR & MRS	NEE
GREAT, GREAT, GREAT-GRANDPARENTS	MR & MRS	NEE
GREAT, GREAT, GREAT-GRANDPARENTS	MR & MRS	NEE
GREAT, GREAT, GREAT-GRANDPARENTS	MR & MRS	NEE
GREAT, GREAT, GREAT-GRANDPARENTS	MR & MRS	NEE
GREAT, GREAT, GREAT-GRANDPARENTS	MR & MRS	NEE
GREAT, GREAT, GREAT-GRANDPARENTS	MR & MRS	NEE
GREAT, GREAT, GREAT-GRANDPARENTS	MR & MRS	NEE
GREAT, GREAT, GREAT-GRANDPARENTS	MR & MRS	NEE
GREAT, GREAT, GREAT-GRANDPARENTS	MR & MRS	NEE
GREAT, GREAT, GREAT-GRANDPARENTS	MR & MRS	NEE
GREAT, GREAT, GREAT-GRANDPARENTS	MR & MRS	NEE
GREAT, GREAT, GREAT-GRANDPARENTS	MR & MRS	NEE
GREAT, GREAT, GREAT-GRANDPARENTS	MR & MRS	NEE
GREAT, GREAT, GREAT-GRANDPARENTS	MR & MRS	NEE
GREAT, GREAT, GREAT-GRANDPARENTS	MR & MRS	NEE
GREAT, GREAT, GREAT-GRANDPARENTS	MR & MRS	NEE
GREAT, GREAT, GREAT-GRANDPARENTS	MR & MRS	NEE
GREAT, GREAT, GREAT-GRANDPARENTS	MR & MRS	NEE
GREAT, GREAT, GREAT-GRANDPARENTS	MR & MRS	NEE

WIFE'S
PHOTOGRAPH

Wife's Family

HER BROTHERS AND SISTERS, NIECES AND NEPHEWS

NAME	BORN	DIED	SPOUSE	CHILDREN

PLACE
PHOTOGRAPH
HERE

PLACE
PHOTOGRAPH
HERE

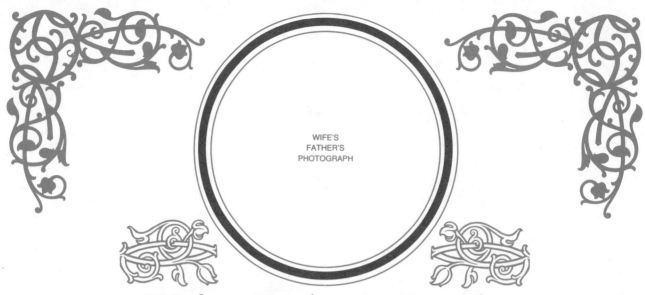

WIFE'S
FATHER'S
PHOTOGRAPH

Wife's Father's Family
HER FATHER, HER UNCLES AND AUNTS AND COUSINS

NAME	BORN	DIED	SPOUSE	CHILDREN

ADDITIONAL INFORMATION

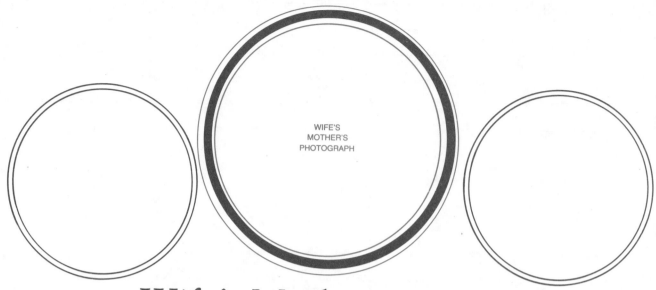

Wife's Mother's Family
HER MOTHER, HER UNCLES AND AUNTS AND COUSINS

NAME	BORN	DIED	SPOUSE	CHILDREN

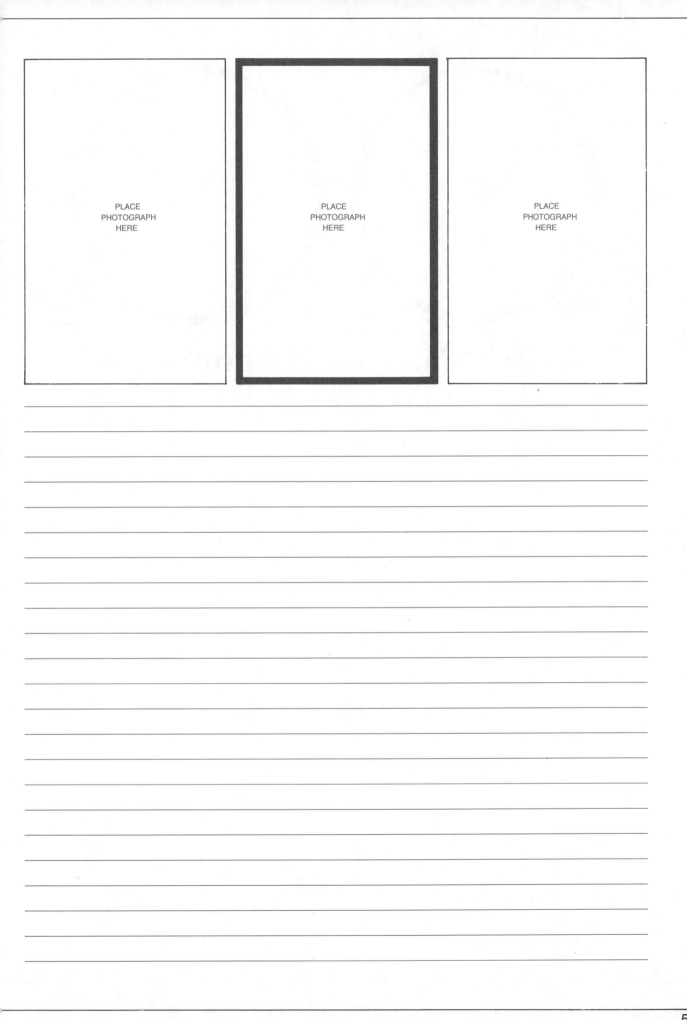

PLACE
PHOTOGRAPH
HERE

PLACE
PHOTOGRAPH
HERE

PLACE
PHOTOGRAPH
HERE

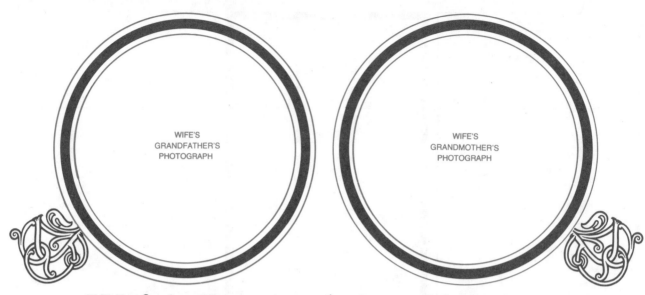

Wife's Paternal Grandparents
WIFE'S GRANDFATHER, HIS GREAT-AUNTS AND UNCLES AND AND THEIR CHILDREN

NAME	BORN	DIED	SPOUSE	CHILDREN

ADDITIONAL INFORMATION

PLACE
PHOTOGRAPH
HERE

PLACE
PHOTOGRAPH
HERE

Wife's Paternal Grandparents
WIFE'S GRANDMOTHER, HER GREAT-AUNTS AND UNCLES
AND THEIR CHILDREN

NAME	BORN	DIED	SPOUSE	CHILDREN

ADDITIONAL INFORMATION

_____
_____
_____
_____
_____
_____
_____
_____
_____
_____
_____
_____

NAME	BORN	DIED	SPOUSE	CHILDREN

PLACE
PHOTOGRAPH
HERE

PLACE
PHOTOGRAPH
HERE

PLACE
PHOTOGRAPH
HERE

Wife's Maternal Grandparents
WIFE'S GRANDFATHER, HER GREAT-AUNTS AND UNCLES
AND THEIR CHILDREN

NAME	BORN	DIED	SPOUSE	CHILDREN

INTERESTING DETAILS _____
_____
_____
_____
_____
_____
_____
_____
_____
_____
_____
_____
_____
_____

NAME	BORN	DIED	SPOUSE	CHILDREN

PLACE
PHOTOGRAPH
HERE

PLACE
PHOTOGRAPH
HERE

NAME _____

NAME _____

Wife's Maternal Grandparents

WIFE'S GRANDMOTHER, HER GREAT-AUNTS AND UNCLES AND THEIR CHILDREN

NAME	BORN	DIED	SPOUSE	CHILDREN

ADDITIONAL INFORMATION

_____
_____
_____
_____
_____
_____
_____
_____
_____
_____
_____
_____
_____
_____
_____
_____
_____
_____
_____
_____
_____
_____

PLACE
PHOTOGRAPH
HERE

PLACE
PHOTOGRAPH
HERE

PLACE
PHOTOGRAPH
HERE

Wife's Paternal Great-Grandparents

GREAT-GRANDFATHER

NAME   BORN   DIED   SPOUSE   CHILDREN

SPECIAL COMMENTS

Wife's Paternal
Great~Grandparents
GREAT-GRANDMOTHER

NAME   BORN   DIED   SPOUSE   CHILDREN

SPECIAL COMMENTS

Wife's Maternal Great~Grandparents

GREAT-GRANDFATHER

NAME   BORN   DIED   SPOUSE   CHILDREN

SPECIAL COMMENTS

Wife's Maternal
Great~Grandparents

GREAT-GRANDMOTHER

NAME	BORN	DIED	SPOUSE	CHILDREN

SPECIAL COMMENTS

Wife's Family Immigration Record

From where did your descendants originally come? When?
How? Why? Where relevant include date of citizenship and
as much additional information as possible.

NAME	EMIGRATED FROM	TO	DATE	TRANSPORT

Add any information describing the migration of your family within this country and so outline how your branch of the family came to settle where it is today.

Wife's Family
War Service Record

NAME

RANK

WHERE SERVED

SPECIAL AWARDS

ADDITIONAL INFORMATION

NAME

RANK

WHERE SERVED

SPECIAL AWARDS

ADDITIONAL INFORMATION

NAME

RANK

WHERE SERVED

SPECIAL AWARDS

ADDITIONAL INFORMATION

NAME

RANK

WHERE SERVED

SPECIAL AWARDS

ADDITIONAL INFORMATION

NAME

RANK

WHERE SERVED

SPECIAL AWARDS

ADDITIONAL INFORMATION

NAME

RANK

WHERE SERVED

SPECIAL AWARDS

ADDITIONAL INFORMATION

NAME

RANK

WHERE SERVED

SPECIAL AWARDS

ADDITIONAL INFORMATION

NAME

RANK

WHERE SERVED

SPECIAL AWARDS

ADDITIONAL INFORMATION

Wife's Family Photographs

NAME	DATE	INTERESTING DETAILS	PLACE

PLACE
PHOTOGRAPH
HERE

PLACE
PHOTOGRAPH
HERE

PLACE
PHOTOGRAPH
HERE

PLACE
PHOTOGRAPH
HERE

PLACE
PHOTOGRAPH
HERE

PLACE
PHOTOGRAPH
HERE

PLACE
PHOTOGRAPH
HERE

PLACE
PHOTOGRAPH
HERE

Weddings

NAMES	DATE	PLACE

PLACE
PHOTOGRAPH
HERE

Weddings

NAMES	DATE	PLACE

NAMES   DATE   PLACE

81

Wedding Photographs

Religious Ceremonies

NAME	CEREMONY	DATE AND PLACE

Where We Worship

Lest We Forget

We all have special memories of those who have died. Here is
an opportunity to record these memories and other special
anecdotes

NAME _____ DATE AND CAUSE OF DEATH _____

_____

_____

_____

_____

_____

_____

_____

_____

_____

_____

_____

_____

_____

_____

_____

_____

_____

_____

_____

_____

_____

_____

NAME

DATE AND CAUSE OF DEATH

Lest We Forget

CONTINUED

NAME   DATE AND CAUSE OF DEATH

Lest We Forget

INTERESTING DETAILS

TERRESTRIAL ORCHIDS

Our Family Homes

Address —————————————————————————————————————
——

Date of purchase ———————————————————————————————
Period of residence: From ————————————————— To ——————————
Other details ———————————————————————————————
——
——

Address ———————————————————————————————————————
——

Date of purchase ————————————————————————————————
Period of residence: From ————————————————— To ——————————
Other details ———————————————————————————————
——
——

Address ———————————————————————————————————————
——

Date of purchase ———————————————————————————————
Period of residence: From ————————————————— To ——————————
Other details ———————————————————————————————
——
——
——
——

Address ——

——

Date of purchase ————————————————————————————————————

Period of residence: From —————————————————— **To** ———————————

Other details —————————————————————————————————————

——

——

Husband's Family Home

Wife's Family Home

Homes of our ancestors

PLACE
PHOTOGRAPH
HERE

PLACE
PHOTOGRAPH
HERE

PLACE
PHOTOGRAPH
HERE

PLACE
PHOTOGRAPH
HERE

PLACE
PHOTOGRAPH
HERE

PLACE
PHOTOGRAPH
HERE

PLACE
PHOTOGRAPH
HERE

Schools Attended

Level of Achievement

NAME	SCHOOL, COLLEGE OR UNIVERSITY	DATES OF ATTENDANCE	QUALIFICATIONS GAINED

NAME	SCHOOL, COLLEGE OR UNIVERSITY	DATES OF ATTENDANCE	QUALIFICATIONS GAINED

Schools Attended

Special Achievements

ACADEMIC	ATHLETIC	ARTISTIC	OTHER

ACADEMIC   ATHLETIC   ARTISTIC   OTHER

Membership of Clubs and Organizations

NAME	ORGANIZATION	OFFICE HELD	DATE

BRIEFLY OUTLINE FUNCTION OF THE ORGANIZATION

_____

_____

_____

_____

_____

_____

_____

_____

NAME	ORGANIZATION	OFFICE HELD	DATE

Employment Profiles

EMPLOYER/COMPANY	POSITIONS HELD	DATE

SPECIAL COMMENTS

Family Business Enterprises

Record information about any member of your family who may have experienced an interesting employment/business history, including reasons for successes and/or failures.

Family Sporting Activities

NAME _____

SPORT _____ LEVEL OF ACHIEVEMENT _____

DETAILS _____
_____

NAME _____

SPORT _____ LEVEL OF ACHIEVEMENT _____

DETAILS _____
_____

NAME _____

SPORT _____ LEVEL OF ACHIEVEMENT _____

DETAILS _____
_____

NAME _____

SPORT _____ LEVEL OF ACHIEVEMENT _____

DETAILS _____
_____

NAME _____

SPORT _____ LEVEL OF ACHIEVEMENT _____

DETAILS _____
_____

NAME _____

SPORT _____ LEVEL OF ACHIEVEMENT _____

DETAILS _____
_____

Special Friends

Most families, or family members have special friends who virtually become a member of that family and share in its joys and sorrows. Record details of meeting and particular anecdotes which bring fond memories.

PLACE
PHOTOGRAPH
HERE

PLACE
PHOTOGRAPH
HERE

PLACE
PHOTOGRAPH
HERE

Family Pets

Whether it be four-legged, feathered, scaled or furry, the family pet inevitably becomes a member of the family, sharing your daily activities, or running them. Recall your pets; how they were obtained and describe the special antics which remain notable.

OWNER	PET'S NAME	TYPE OF PET	DATE

Family Vehicle

Can you recall your first car? List all the vehicles you have
owned and in a small way record the progress of the motor car
in history. Also describe the various adventures experienced
with them.

OWNER	MAKE	MODEL	YEAR	YEAR OF OWNERSHIP

Family Holidays

Some holidays may have lasted only a few days, others may
have been more spectacular, travelling to exotic places; but
all produce special memories and often introduce us to new
experiences and more importantly, new friends.

DATE   LOCATION   SPECIAL FEATURES

Heirlooms and Family Collections

Most families include a collector, whether it be of match
boxes or paintings. Record details of each collection — who
began it, why, how much was collected.
List all family heirlooms, mentioning the original owner and
how the items were passed on to succeeding generations. Try
to discover any special details about the heirlooms: why they
have assumed their importance.

Heirlooms and Family Collections

CONTINUED

Special Family Occasions

There are always special events which require a family celebration, be they birthdays, anniversaries or reunions. List these special occasions, including who was there, where it was held etc. and help recall the highs and lows of the event.

Special Family Occasions

CONTINUED

CONTINUED

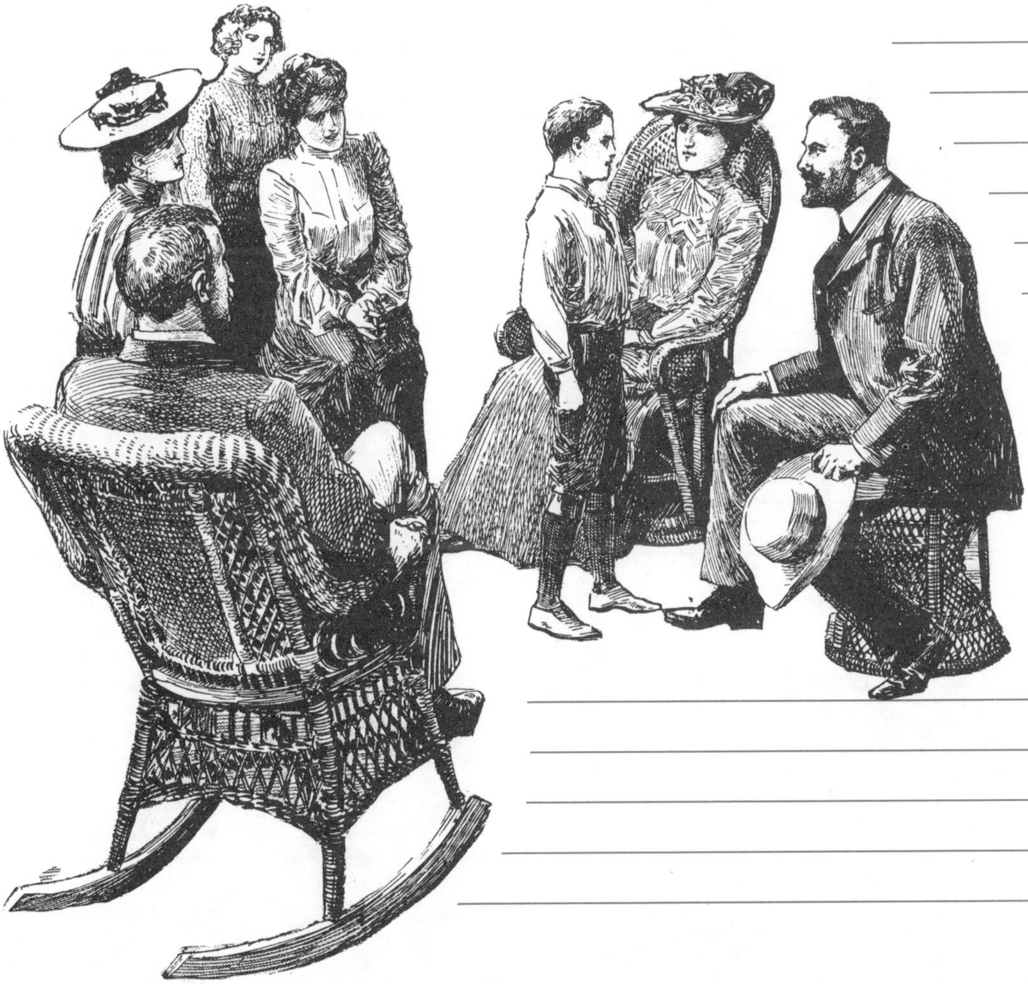

Family Traditions

What traditions do your family keep up? How have these habits developed?

Storytellers

Each family has at least one storyteller who can fill the gaps and recall experiences which seem minor but which colour our family history. Until these stories are written down they are in danger of being lost forever. Catch up with the storytellers in your family and convert oral history into a written account for all to enjoy.

Storytellers

CONTINUED